This book belongs to

_____

ISBN-10: 0998286206
ISBN-13: 978-0998286204

Published by Edible Rainbow Project Press
Middletown, NY 10940

www.ediblerainbowproject.com

Anise Loves GREEN Food

For Claire and Eve
-Mama

This is Anise.
She's going to be a chef.

That's her brother, Matisse.
He's going to be a painter.

They have something in common.
They both love food.

He loves to eat.
She loves to cook.
(Obviously.)

Today, they also love the color green.

Anise loves bowls full of green grapes.
She also loves rolling down grassy hills.

Matisse loves crunchy green apples.
He also loves caterpillars and lizards.

"I'm hungry," says Matisse.

"You're always hungry, Matisse," says Anise.

"Actually, I'm hungry too."

"But Mom and Dad are out," says Matisse.

"Then, we can cook something," Anise says.

"Grilled cheeses?" he asks.

"Not today. Today I want to eat green," says Anise.

"You can't eat a color, Anise!" Matisse exclaims.

"Sure you can. Let's go see what we can find,"

replies Anise.

Anise and Matisse run to the kitchen to look for green food.

What do they find?

They find:
A bunch of kale
A head of broccoli
Some herbs; parsley, basil and mint
4 zucchinis
A couple of leeks...

6 kiwis

3 pears

5 green apples

2 avocados

A bunch of asparagus

and 12 cucumbers.

"WOW! That's a lot.
Are you sure it's a good idea to eat all this green?"
asks Matisse.

"Of course it is! Let's look through these cookbooks
 for some ideas," says Anise.

"Mmm. How do you feel about Creamy Broccoli Soup?" asks Anise.

"I'd rather eat something else," says Matisse, unconvinced.

"I want to try it. We can bake a loaf of bread to go with it. Oooh and we can have these Kale Chips too, and Cricket Cupcakes for dessert!" Anise says confidently.

Matisse thinks about it but would still rather eat something else.

"I kind of want to try this minty pesto actually," says Matisse curiously.

"Oh, that sounds good!" answers Anise.

"I'm thirsty. Can we drink green, too?"
Matisse asks.

"YES, we can!" says Anise. "Let's see, avocado, mint, limes, oh and a mango! We can make a smoothie."

"I don't want to drink that," Matisse says worriedly. "It doesn't sound good at all."

"But it is good," Anise promises.

"I don't know." Matisse is still suspicious and still thirsty.

In the kitchen, Matisse reads to Anise.

"Cut broccoli into florets. Tear leaves of kale and drizzle olive oil over leaves. Add a pinch of salt."

"Place herbs in blender."

Anise listens carefully. She is in awe with every step. The herbs are delicate but fresh. The kale is a deep and cool green. The sautéing leeks fill the kitchen with a sweet aroma.

Soon after:

The kale chips go bake, bake, bake.

The pasta boils bubble, bubble, bubble.

The pesto goes blend, blend, blend.

Matisse gets distracted. He's looking at recipes. He's painting. He's getting hungrier and hungrier.

"Oh, can we make these green ice lollies? We have almost all the ingredients for them." Matisse is now very excited and very hungry.

Anise just nods. Anise is focused.

Her chef's knife goes
chop, chop, chop.

Her wooden spoons go stir, stir, stir.

The sautéing leeks go
sizzle, sizzle, sizzle.

The kitchen is singing, yet, once in a while Anise stops to
daydream about running her own kitchen someday.

The soup is simmering.

The smoothie is ready.

The bread is done.

The cupcakes are cool.

The delicious smell of the food cooking greet Mom and Dad when they get home.

"Mmmm...so what's on the menu, kids?" asks Mom.
"Can you guess?" asks Anise.

Mom closes her eyes and lets her nose do the work.
"I smell leeks and parsley, garlic and mint?"

"Well done, Mom! We're having Kale chips, Creamy Broccoli Soup and Sunflower Pesto," says Anise proudly.

"I smell something sweet and chocolatey," says Dad.
"They're Cricket Cupcakes!" Anise answers excitedly.

"Don't forget my smoothie," says Matisse, who tasted it and loved it.

"Here it is, Mom, a magic green smoothie of..."

Mom interrupts, "Let me guess, mint, mango, lime?"

"And avocado!" says Anise.

"Nom, nom," says Matisse.

"Nom, nom is right. Can we help?" asks Dad.
They each grab an apron and get to work.

"What's the occasion for the green menu?" Dad asks them.
"I love green food," says Anise.
"It's soft, juicy and crunchy. It's also bitter, sweet and sour.
It amazes me."

Matisse adds, "Green food is so different even though it's all green. It's so tasty and I love it too."

"OK, let's eat!"

"Bon Appetit," Anise says.

The family sits around the table eating the delicious food they've prepared.

"Nom, nom. Thanks, Anise," says Matisse.

Matisse then has a thought, "I wonder what it's like to eat red?"

Just with that thought, Anise is already planning her red menu.

RECIPES

Anise and Matisse are delighted to share some of the recipes they've found, created, and cooked together. These are their favorites. Which one is your favorite?

Roasted Lemony Asparagus (V, GF)
Avocado Toast (V)
Zucchini Fritters (Vg, GF)
Sunflower Pesto (V)
Velvety Cream Broccoli Soup (Vg, GF)
Cucumber Carrot Tomato Salad (V, GF)
Crispy Kale Chips (V, GF)
Overnight Oats-Pears, Blueberries, Cranberries (V, GF)
Chocolate Avocado Mousse (V, GF)
Kiwi Melon Ice Lollies (V, GF)
Cricket Cupcakes (Vg, GF)
Avocado Mango Mint Smoothie (V, GF)

P.S. Anise wants you to know that
C=cup, T=tablespoon and t=teaspoon
GF: Gluten Free   Vg: Vegetarian   V: Vegan

Happy Cooking!

Roasted Lemony Asparagus

Serves a family of 4

V, GF

Anise really likes these with some quinoa and scrambled eggs.

You'll need:
- 1 pound asparagus, trimmed
- 2 T extra virgin olive oil
- 1 T freshly squeezed lemon juice
- 1 t lemon zest
- ½t sea salt or Himalayan Pink salt
- 1 T parsley, chopped

To make:
Heat oven to 350°F/180°C

1. Line a baking sheet with parchment paper.
2. Lay asparagus neatly in rows on baking sheet and drizzle oil, lemon juice, lemon zest and salt. Toss until well coated and arrange so asparagus are next to each other, happily.
3. Roast for 25 minutes or until just tender with a little bite.
4. Sprinkle asparagus with parsley when out of the oven so it looks like green snowflakes are resting on them.

Enjoy!

Avocado Toast

Serves a family of 4

This is Anise's and Matisse's favorite for breakfast, lunch AND dinner!

You'll need:
- 2 T extra virgin olive oil
- 4 chunky slices of your favorite toast
- 2 ripe avocados
- Coarse sea salt, to taste

To make:
1. Slice the avocado lengthwise all the way around.
2. Twist the avocado to release it and scoop out the yummy, creamy avocado.
3. Drizzle ½ T of the olive oil on your toast and smear on the avocado.
4. Sprinkle salt over the avocado.
5. If you're adding extra toppings, now is the time to do it

Optional toppings include:
roasted cherry tomatoes, mozzarella cheese, medium boiled egg, fresh herbs, corn and Anise's favorite is adding the Roasted Lemony Asparagus!

Enjoy over and over again!

Zucchini Fritters

Makes about 3 dozen fritters

These are Matisse's favorite snack.

You'll need:
- 1 clove garlic, minced
- 1 leek, finely sliced, white and light green parts (about ¼ C)
- 3 T fresh mint, chopped
- 2 T freshly squeezed lemon juice
- Zest of 1 lemon
- 1 t sea salt or Himalayan Pink Salt
- Freshly ground black pepper, to taste
- 3 C shredded zucchini
- 2 eggs, lightly beaten
- 3 T brown rice flour
- 3 T buckwheat flour
- 2-3 T extra virgin olive oil

To make:
1. In a bowl, add the garlic, leek, mint, lemon juice and zest, salt and pepper and combine well. Add the flour in steps, slowly mixing it into the mixture.
2. Add zucchini and eggs and stir well until thoroughly combined.
3. Heat 2 T of oil in a skillet over medium heat.
4. Using a tablespoon to measure, drop batter into skillet and pan fry, listen for the sizzle, for 4-5 minutes before turning over and cooking for another couple of minutes until golden brown.
5. Place the fritters on a wire rack over a sheet pan to cool slightly.
6. Repeat and add oil as needed.

*This goes great with the pesto as a dip! **Enjoy!**

Sunflower Pesto
Serves a family of 4

Matisse and Anise LOVE this dish with vegetables and
they eat this for lunch AND dinner!

You'll need:
- 1 pound pasta
- 1 T extra virgin olive oil
- 1 C mint leaves
- 1 C parsley leaves
- 1 garlic clove, minced
- ½C sunflower seeds
- ¼C pasta water
- ¼C extra virgin olive oil
- 2 T lemon juice
- 1 t lemon zest
- ½ - 1 t sea salt (plus more for pasta water)

To make:
1. In a large soup pot, boil 8 C of water, add a big pinch of salt and get to a rolling boil.
2. Add pasta and cook according to package instructions.
3. When pasta is done, drain and rinse under cold water to stop the cooking. Drizzle with olive oil
4. Place all pesto ingredients in a food processor or blender and blend until smooth. Do a little dance while it's blending. You may need to add more liquid to reach a creamy consistency.
5. Put pasta in a bowl and toss with pesto. They're ready for the party.

*Variation: This dish is even more delicious with some sauteed broccoli and zucchini tossed with the pasta.

Enjoy!

Velvety Cream Broccoli Soup

Vg, GF

Serves a family of 4

Matisse wasn't sure he'd like this soup, but Anise was right. It's so creamy and so yummy!

You'll need:

- 2 T butter or extra virgin olive oil
- 1 large leek, thinly sliced to tender greens (about 1/2 C)
- 1 stalk celery, diced
- 1 medium carrot, diced
- 1-2 Yukon or Russet potato, diced (about 1 C)
- ½t salt
- ¼t ground cumin
- Freshly ground pepper to taste
- 1 pound of broccoli, cut into florets, stems peeled and cut
- 5 C vegetable stock or water
- 1 T freshly squeezed lemon juice
- Grated Parmigiano Reggiano for garnish

To make:

1. Heat the butter or olive oil in a soup pot over medium heat and add leek. Sauté until tender.
2. Add celery, carrot, potatoes and salt, pepper, cumin and sauté until tender, about 7-5 minutes.
3. Add ½C broth to the pot to deglaze the pot and add the broccoli. Lower heat to medium, cover and cook until the broccoli is a lovely bright green color, about 4-5 minutes.
4. In a blender, add 2C of the broth and half of the broccoli mixture from the pot. Blend until creamy smooth. Pour creamy soup into a large bowl.
5. Repeat with remaining broth and broccoli mixture and add to bowl.
6. Rinse out pot and add the soup, placing it over low heat. Add lemon juice and heat through for 8-10 minutes.
7. Serve with grated Parmigiano Reggiano sprinkled on top. **Enjoy!**

Cucumber and Carrot Salad

Serves a family of 4

This is the first salad that Matisse ever loved. Now he eats all kinds of salads.

You'll need:
- 2 cucumbers, large dice (about 2 C)
- 2 carrots, cut on diagonal (about 1 C)
- ½C of cherry tomatoes, halved
- 1 T chopped basil

To make:
1. Mix all ingredients in a bowl.
2. Divide among four bowls and drizzle with dressing.*

*For the dressing:
Anise prefers just a drizzle of olive oil and a squeeze of lemon juice. Matisse likes the dressing below.

You'll need:
- 2 T extra virgin olive oil
- 2 T apple cider vinegar
- 1 t dijon mustard
- 2 t maple syrup
- 1 t lemon juice
- Pinch of sea salt

To make:
Whisk all ingredients together until well mixed and then drizzle over salad.

Enjoy!

Crispy Kale Chips

V, GF

Serves a family of 4

Anise and Matisse can not get enough
of these!

You'll need:

- 1 bunch of curly kale
- 1 T extra virgin olive oil
- Sea salt, to taste

To make:

Heat oven to 300°F/150°C

1. Tear leaves into large pieces and remove completely from the stems.
2. Wash and thoroughly dry leaves.
3. Drizzle the olive oil over the leaves and rub the oil into the leaves. Get the oil into those little grooves so that everything is coated well.
4. On a baking sheet prepared with parchment paper, spread the kale in one even layer.
5. Sprinkle salt over leaves.
6. Bake chips for 12 minutes and then rotate the sheet pan and bake for 12 more minutes.
7. Remove kale when it's dried and crispy and let cool for a few minutes before diving in.

Enjoy!

Overnight Oats
Pears, Blueberries, Cranberries

V, GF

Serves a family of 4

Matisse LOVES this breakfast., but he warms
it up. Anise loves it chilled.

You'll need:
- 1 ripe banana, mashed
- 2 T chia seeds
- 1 T pumpkin seeds
- ½t ground cinnamon
- ¼t freshly grated nutmeg
- ½C unsweetened shredded coconut
- ¼C dried cranberries
- 1 C rolled oats
- 1 ½C milk (Anise prefers coconut, but regular milk works great, too!)
- ¼t vanilla extract (optional)
- 2 green pears, diced
- ½C fresh or frozen blueberries
- ½C raw walnuts, chopped

To make:
1. In a medium sized bowl, mash the banana until no clumps are left.
   Stir in the chia seeds, pumpkin seeds, cinnamon, nutmeg, coconut and
   cranberries.
2. Next, stir in the oats, milk and vanilla extract. Mix well to incorporate all
   ingredients.
3. Cover with plastic wrap or a lid and refrigerate overnight.
4. Good morning! Now, serve oatmeal in individual jars, top with pears,
   blueberries and walnuts.

Enjoy your morning and your oats!

Chocolatey Avocado Mousse

Serves a family of 4

Anise and Matisse LOVE this dessert. They especially love to use fresh berries and crunchy nuts for toppings.

You'll need:
- 2 ripe avocados
- ½C coconut milk (or cream)
- ¼C cacao powder
- 3 T raw honey or maple syrup
- 1 t vanilla extract
- 1 t ground cinnamon

To make:
1. Place all ingredients in a food processor and process until super smooth.
2. Divide mousse into 4 ramekins and refrigerate for 4 hours or overnight.
3. Top with optional toppings before serving.

Optional toppings include:
Unsweetened shredded coconut, hemp seeds, toasted walnuts or almonds, fresh or frozen raspberries, strawberries, blueberries or red currants. **Enjoy!**

Kiwi Melon Ice Lollies

V, GF

Makes 6 Lollies

Anise and Matisse love these on warm summer days, especially after a good time at the playground.

You'll need:
- 4 Kiwis, peeled and scooped out
- 2 C honeydew melon, rough chop
- 2 T lemon juice
- 3 T raw honey or maple syrup

To make:
1. Place all ingredients in a food processor and process, on lowest setting, until all chunks of fruit are smooth. Try to avoid breaking too many seeds because it could cause the lollies to taste bitter.
2. Pour liquid into molds and freeze.

Enjoy!

Cricket Cupcakes

Makes 6 cupcakes

You'll need:
- ¼C coconut flour
- ¼C organic cocoa powder
- ¼C coconut sugar or maple sugar
- 1 t ground cinnamon
- ¼t baking soda
- ½t baking powder
- 4 large eggs (at room temperature)
- ¼C + 2 T coconut oil
- 2 T raw honey
- 2 T coconut milk (or other milk)
- 1 t vanilla extract
- 1 t lemon juice
- Pinch of Celtic sea salt

To make:
Heat oven to 350°F/180°C

1. In a large bowl, combine the dry ingredients: coconut flour, cocoa powder, sweetener, cinnamon, baking soda, baking powder and sea salt.
2. In a separate bowl, combine the eggs, coconut oil, honey, coconut milk, vanilla extract, and lemon juice.
3. Add the dry ingredients to the wet and mix to combine.
4. Fill cupcake liners evenly with the batter and bake for 20-25 minutes or until a toothpick inserted into the cupcakes comes out clean.
5. Allow to cool before topping or piping with the frosting.

For the frosting:

You'll need:
- 1 C coconut butter, softened
- ¼C maple syrup
- 2 T raw honey
- ¼C arrowroot starch (more as needed)
- 1 t vanilla extract
- ¼t spirulina powder
- 2 t peppermint extract (optional)*
- 4 mint leaves (optional)

To make:
1. Mix all ingredients in a food processor and set aside.
2. You may need to add some water, ½t at a time, to achieve the creamy consistency you're looking for.

*If your kids LOVE mint, then please add this to your frosting, but a lot of kids don't so the green coconut version is just as delicious.

Enjoy!

Adapted from Melissa Christy Maidana at www.solfood365.com

Avocado Mango Mint Smoothie

V, GF

Serves a family of 4

Matisse was SO surprised how delicious this smoothie
was. Anise KNEW it would be amazing. What do
you think of it?

You'll need:

- 1/2 hass avocado
- 2 1/2 C frozen mango
- 10-15 largish mint leaves, chopped
- 1 C water or coconut water
- 1/2 C coconut milk
- 1 T ground hemp seeds
- 1 T maple syrup
- 1 T coconut oil
- 1 t freshly squeezed lime juice

To make:

Place all ingredients in a blender and blend until
blissfully smooth. You won't need ice unless
you use fresh fruit, in which case,
add 4 ice cubes.

Enjoy!

The End

Made in the USA
Lexington, KY
15 December 2016